CW00393685

Violin
Grade 8

Pieces

for Trinity College London exams

2016-2019

Published by
Trinity College London
www.trinitycollege.com

Registered in England
Company no. 02683033
Charity no. 1014792

Printed in England by Caligraving Ltd.

TCL 014887
ISBN 978-0-85736-461-6

9 780857 364616

Adagio

2nd movt from Concerto in E major

Johann Sebastian Bach
(1685–1750)

3

Hornpipe Rondo

from Violin Concerto

Ed. Tasmin Little

Gerald Finzi
(1901–1956)

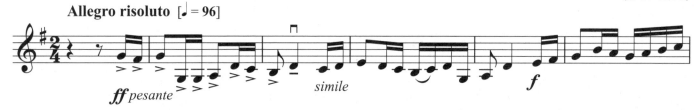

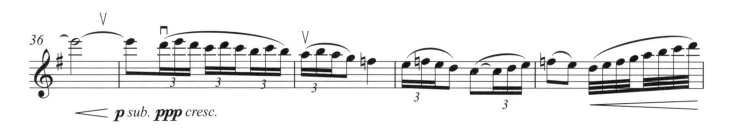

Original tempo ♩ = *c.*120

poco allargando

Pochiss. meno mosso [♩ = c.96]

Tambourin

4th movt from Sonata in D major, op. 9, no. 3

Jean-Marie Leclair
(1697–1764)

Play the first repeat only in the exam.

Dudziarz

(The Bagpipe Player)

Henryk Wieniawski
(1835–1880)

Sonatensatz

(Scherzo from F-A-E Sonata)

Johannes Brahms
(1833–1897)

Play the repeat in the exam.

Nocturne

Aaron Copland
(1900–1990)

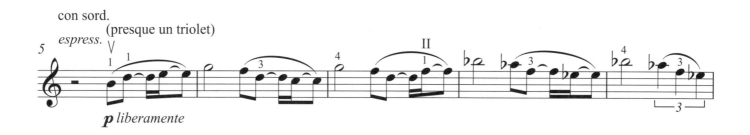

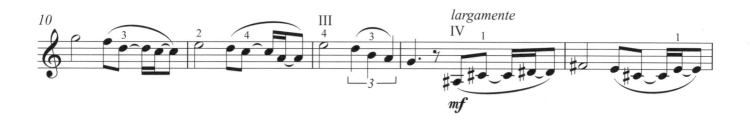

Elégie

from Suite for Violin and Orchestra

Arr. Robert Threlfall

Frederick Delius
(1862–1934)

After the Tryst

James MacMillan
(born 1959)

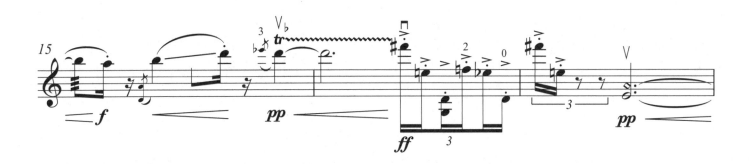

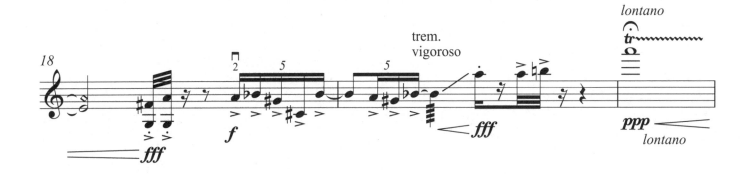

Bizarrerie

Edward Elgar
(1857–1934)

© Copyright 2015 by Trinity College London.

Violin
Grade 8

Pieces
for Trinity College London exams

2016-2019

Published by
Trinity College London
www.trinitycollege.com

Registered in England
Company no. 02683033
Charity no. 1014792

Adagio

2nd movt from Concerto in E major

Johann Sebastian Bach
(1685–1750)

4

Hornpipe Rondo

from Violin Concerto

Ed. Tasmin Little

Gerald Finzi
(1901–1956)

Original tempo ♩ = *c.*120

6

poco allargando

Pochiss. meno mosso [♩ = c.96]

accel. poco a poco

Tambourin

4th movt from Sonata in D major, op. 9, no. 3

Jean-Marie Leclair
(1697–1764)

Play the first repeat only in the exam.

16

Dudziarz

(The Bagpipe Player)

Henryk Wieniawski
(1835–1880)

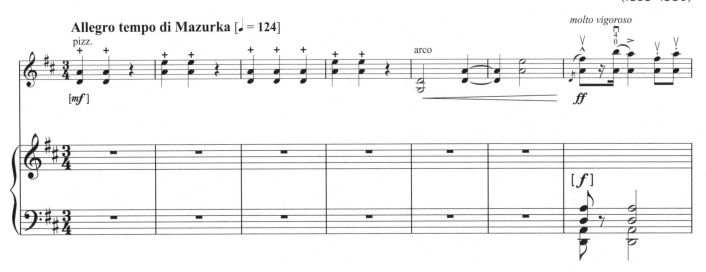

Sonatensatz

(Scherzo from F-A-E Sonata)

Johannes Brahms
(1833–1897)

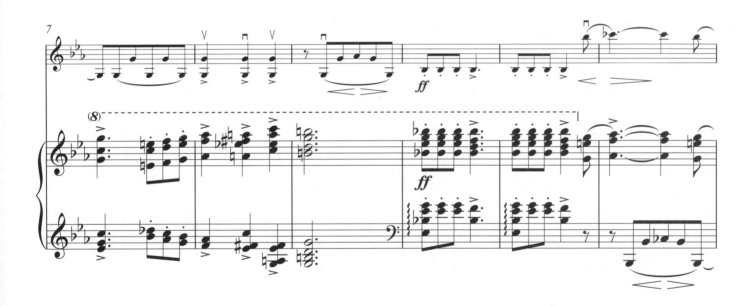

Play the repeat in the exam.

26

Trio

Più moderato [♩ = 68]

*sempre **ff** e grandioso*

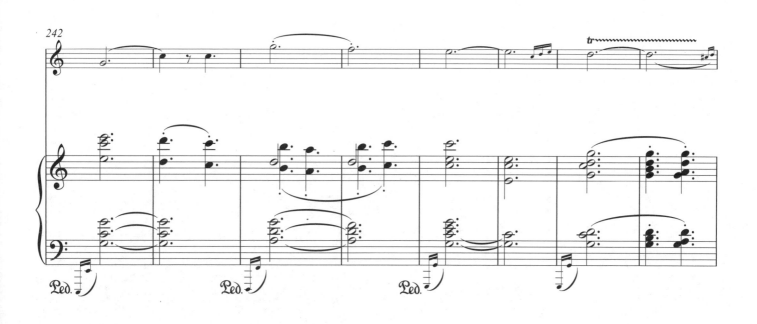

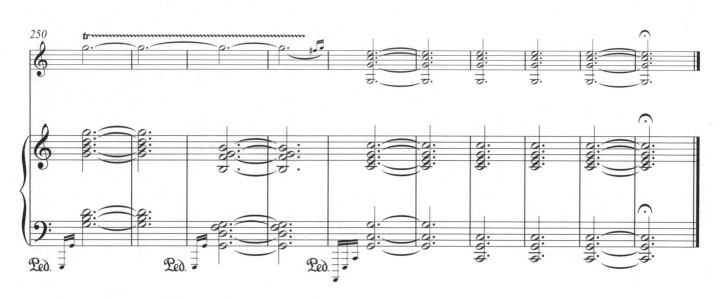

Nocturne

Aaron Copland
(1900–1990)

Tempo I (Lento moderato)

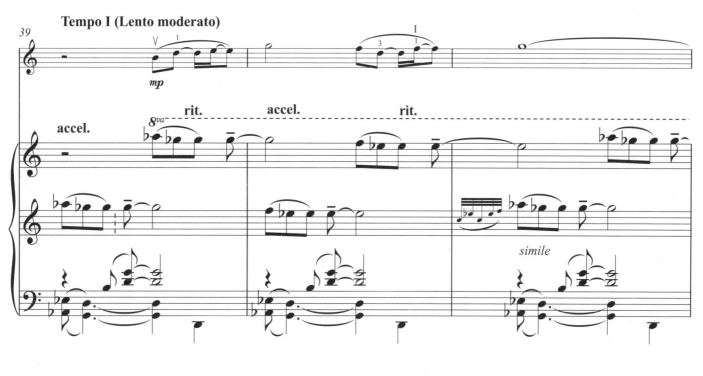

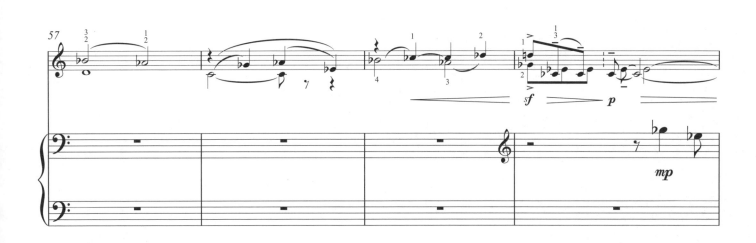

Elégie
from Suite for Violin and Orchestra

Arr. Robert Threlfall

Frederick Delius
(1862–1934)

After the Tryst

James MacMillan
(born 1959)

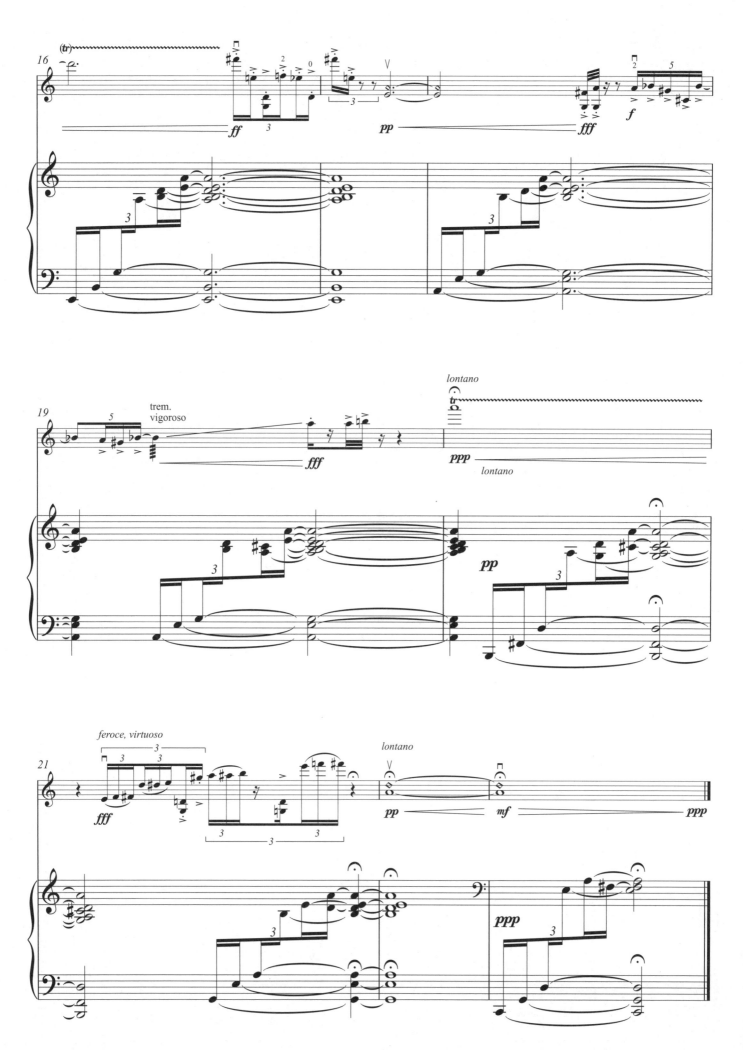

Bizarrerie

Edward Elgar
(1857–1934)

Poco più lento

54

(continued from inside front cover)

Technical work – Candidates to prepare i) Bowing exercise

i) Bowing exercise (from memory):

Candidates should choose one of the Grade 8 scales and the examiner will choose any one of the specified bowings from Grades 5-7 and ask the candidate to play the scale with that bowing.

Candidates to prepare in full *either* section ii) *or* section iii)

either **ii) Scales, arpeggios & technical exercises** (from memory):

Candidates should prepare major and minor scales and arpeggios from the following tonal centres, to be played with separate bows *or* slurred as requested by the examiner.

G, A, Bb, Db/C# and Eb	three octaves	min. tempi: scales: ♩ = 88 arpeggios: ♩ = 88 7ths: ♩ = 92	scales separate bows *or* slurred three octaves to a bow (one bow up and one bow down, with a change of bow on the top note); arpeggios separate bows *or* slurred nine notes to a bow
Plus: Chromatic scales starting on Bb, C and D	two octaves		separate bows *or* slurred twelve notes to a bow
Diminshed 7ths starting on A#, C and D			separate bows *or* slurred eight notes to a bow

Major tonal centre

When the examiner requests a major tonal centre, the candidate should play in succession:

> The major scale
> The major arpeggio
> The dominant 7th starting on that note and resolving onto the tonic
> (to be prepared with separate bows and slurred two crotchet beats to a bow)

Minor tonal centre

When the examiner requests a minor tonal centre, the candidate should play in succession:

> The melodic minor scale
> The harmonic minor scale
> The minor arpeggio

Technical exercises (from memory) [♩ = 88]:

a) Bb major in thirds (two octaves):

 etc

b) G major in sixths (two octaves):

 etc

c) D major in octaves (one octave):

 etc

or **iii) Orchestral extracts** (music may be used):

Candidates to prepare 1a *or* 1b; 2a *or* 2b; and 3a *or* 3b (three extracts in total).

The candidate will choose one extract to play first; the examiner will then select one of the remaining two prepared extracts to be performed.

The extracts are contained in *The Orchestral Violinist book 2 (ed. Rodney Friend)* published by Boosey & Hawkes (9790060115967).

1a. Mendelssohn: Symphony no. 4 [III], page 2 (bars 126 to 160) 1b. Wagner: Die Meistersinger von Nürnberg [Overture], pages 24-25 (bars 158 to 178)	for tone and phrasing
2a. Brahms: Symphony no. 4 [IV], page 15 (bars 33 to 40 *and* bars 65 to 73) 2b. Prokofieff: Romeo and Juliet Suite no. 1 [V. Masks], page 30 (fig. 48 to end of extract)	for bowing
3a. Glinka: Russlan and Ludmilla [Overture], page 36 (bar 21 to 7th bar of fig. A) 3b. Moussorgsky, orch. Ravel: Pictures at an Exhibition [3. Tuileries], page 26 (entire extract)	for left hand technique

Supporting tests – candidates to prepare i) *and* ii)

i) sight reading	**ii) aural** *or* **improvisation**

Please refer to the current syllabus for details on all elements of the exam.